GORDON HAS
harry's b

Piano Vocal Guitar

Published 2002
© International Music Publications Ltd
Griffin House 161 Hammersmith Road London W6 8BS England

Edited by Chris Harvey
Folio design by Dominic Brookman
Music Arranged by Artemis Music Ltd
Cover photo by Mike Inns
Design by www.summerhouse.co.uk

In extreme circumstances we see the truth laid out before us. Just when we had begun to accept cynicism as the norm, our humanity runs to our rescue, showing how plainly we all depend on each other to survive in this world. Showing us the grace and beauty in unselfishness. Showing us the real heroes in life are not the celebrities grabbing the headlines, but those unseen all around us, the humble man or woman in the street. Stranger helping stranger united by the most powerful force on Earth that each and every one of us are blessed with and sometimes forget, namely, the innate desire to love and be loved and simply by following higher instincts we can all make that difference.

It's comforting to know how wonderful you are.

Gordon Haskell

how wonderful you are

Words and Music by Gordon Haskell

Bar.

Though we've on - ly___ just be - gun,___

this show will run and run,___ do you know___ how won - der - ful you

are?

are?   Do you   know___ how won-der-ful___ you   are?_____   Do you

know_____   how won - der-ful   you   are?_____

all the time in the world

Words and Music by Gordon Haskell

voodoo dance

Words and Music by Gordon Haskell

When-ev-er you do— that voo - doo,— it puts me in a trance.— Why don't you

sunshine in the night

Words and Music by Gordon Haskell

Dia - mond pearls and pots of gold, few and far be - tween, and a
run - nin' scared on emp - ty, bare - ly keep - in' pace, but you
Am7 Bm7 Cmaj7 D7
love that's made in hea - ven so ve - - - - ry sel - dom
brought me to a stand - still, trea - - - - sur - ing your
Em7 Bm7 Am7 Bm7
seen.
grace.
Yeah, yeah, yeah.
Em7 Bm7 Am7 Bm7 Am7 Bm7
Love - ly la - dy, what have I done? I got sun - shine and moon - light

freeway to her dreams

Words and Music by Gordon Haskell

Verse 3:
I loved her then I love her still
Though it's not what she believes
One day I hope she'll see me there
On the freeway to her dreams.

al capone

Words and Music by Gordon Haskell

D.%. al Coda

Then we'll put on

there goes my heart again

Words and Music by Gordon Haskell

And I don't know where I'm go - ing now,
And I don't think I'll be hang - ing round,
And I don't know where I'm go - ing now,

where to start or ev - en how.
some - thing inside just hit the ground.
where to start or ev - en how.

roll with it

Words and Music by Gordon Haskell

You can

half a chance— you're gon - na take it. 'Cos

in your heart you know— we're gon - na make it. So don't

re - fuse.— You got - ta learn to roll with it.

Verse 3:
You got an appetite
So why not feed it?
It's gonna taste real good,
You're gonna wanna eat it.
And it ain't make believe,
Once you've seen it.
You can give it all you've got
And really mean it.

So don't shake your head *etc.*

feelin' loose

Words and Music by Gordon Haskell

Verse 3:
Too much of anything just weighs me down
I much prefer to travel light.
Too many people want to talk about
Who is wrong and who is right,
I ain't gonna do it,
I see right through it,
It's what brings ev'rybody down.
I'm gonna take my chances on tomorrow
'Til they put me in the ground.

I'm feelin' loose *etc.*

someone i knew

Words and Music by Gordon Haskell

Verse 3:
But these are early days
And you can bet
A whisper over for so long ain't over yet.
I still believe that love was true

When I think about *etc.*

all in the scheme of things

Words and Music by Gordon Haskell

Lyrics:

All the Pha-raohs got to-geth-er when things went on the
A - ri - sto - tle hit the bot - tle, and Pla - to loved the
theo - ries like Py - - tha - go - rus were there for you to

skids, they said, be - fore we go we ough - ta
blow, he said, one plus one we
use, while you ex - plored the

a little help from you

Words and Music by Gordon Haskell

An-y-time you want to talk it____ through,__ I'll be sit-ting

wait-ing for my__ cue,__ if there's an-y-thing I can__